THE WEANS

THE WEANS

ROBERT NATHAN

Alfred A. Knopf   New York

1960

L. C. catalog card number: 60–12962

THIS IS A BORZOI BOOK, PUBLISHED BY ALFRED A. KNOPF, INC.

Some of the material in this book appeared earlier in different form in Harper's Magazine.

To CLARA GRUNTAL,

who has always had the gift of laughter

THE WEANS

PLATE I.

THE WEANS

Those of you who have followed the work of our archaeologists along the east and west coasts of the Great West, or Salt, Continent, and in the interior deserts, know that the Kenya and Uganda expeditions have recently discovered traces of a lost people of prehistory among the mounds and tumuli of that unexplored waste. A few years ago nothing whatever was known about these people, except for an occasional legend in Swahili, or Gullah. And we still know very little about them, to be sure. But now that the inscription on the north wall of the temple at Pound-Laundry on the east coast of the Great West Continent has finally been deciphered by the team led by Sri. B'Han Bollek, we have certain assurance of the theory expressed by Bes Nef, Hanh Shui, and Nat Obelgerst-Levy that communities of considerable extent formerly dotted this salt and desolate land. It is a triumph for those archaeologists who have been busily at work ever since the fortunate discovery of an ivory cross and string of beads at the northeast, or "Bosstin," tumulus, along with a rusted iron wheel which seems to have been designed to run along some kind of track or trolley. These artifacts, as everyone knows, are now in the museum at Kenya.

Late studies, recently completed, place the Wean civilization at its peak or apogee five or six thousand years ago. Who these Weans were, or whence they came, is not known: not only are there definite traces among the artifacts and in the scrolls and glyphs of early European and Mediterranean cultures, including the Hebrew, the Hittite, and the Armenian, but evidence of Polynesian influence, Chinese, Japanese, and Zen. In pictographs from the Valley of the Sun we find the round, bald head and foxy expression of the Sumerian, and—

PLATE II.

some four hundred miles further north—bearded figures with trumpets. These may possibly be Minoan.

But although it is possible that the Weans had some kind of music, no sounds have come down to us from those far-away people except a high, rasping cry from a slender horn-like object found in Oleens.

It is true that no human bones have so far turned up. No Wean skeletons have survived, though a team of anthropologists led by Hulay-Beneker did discover several small lumps of calcium in n.Yok which might possibly have been arthritic deposits. Nevertheless, the contemptuous claim by early Volgarian scholars that the Weans were, in effect, subhuman can now, in the light of recent findings, be summarily dismissed.

Furthermore, in almost all mounds, our workmen have dug up porcelain receptacles of unmistakable shape and purpose, such as are still to be found—though in more primitive form —among the ruins which line the Volga, the Danube, and the Don. The conclusion that the Weans were as human as the Volgarians is inescapable.[1]

[1] *See* infra, *p. 34. (Ed.)*

As we have noted, the origins of these ancient peoples are shrouded in mystery. They may have crossed one or the other of the great oceans, from the east, or from the west, on huge rafts; or possibly both, at the same time. The scholar Bes Nef finds in their language word-roots belonging to the Ethiopian, while his wife, Sra. Bess Nebby, uncovers traces of classical Latin. Both Hulay-Beneker and Professor Kowly of the Institute for Ancient Arts and Letters are inclined to relate the Weans to early forest hunters of the north; while Hanh Shui believes that they may have been Brythons, descendants of a Neolithic people whose upright stones are still to be seen in the Isle of Angles. Professor Shui bases this theory upon a certain similarity in the two glyphs, the Brythonic "bathe" and the Wean "bath"; but his theory necessarily comes to grief when one examines the glyph for "that which rises"—the Brythonic "lift" and the Wean "elevator" having obviously no common root.

Sri. B'Han Bollek has called these people the Weans, because certain archaeological findings incline him to the belief that they called their land the WE, or the US; actually, in the southern part of the continent, the word "Weuns" (or "Weans") does appear, as well as the glyph for Wealls, and the word "Theyuns."

The greatest difficulty in reconstructing the life of the Weans has not been the deciphering of the inscriptions and the scrolls—due to the brilliant work of Professors Bollek and Shui—but the fact that the Weans, unlike the true ancients, used little gold, preferring to build everything of steel or other metal, and of some curious substance which Bes Nef translates as "gastric," or "plastric." As a result, little is left for the archaeologist. Stone was used mainly for monuments, as was bronze, but those which have been uncovered are too heavily encrusted with bird-droppings to be easily recognizable. One theory is that the Weans collected guano; but it is not known what they did with it.

The Weans were probably not at all a friendly or hospitable people—a theory which is based on two recent discoveries, both on the east coast. In the first place, there was recently excavated from the earth of a small island in the ocean just beyond the terminal land-mass at n.Yok, a hollow figure—or at least part of one—of what appears to be a giantess, or possibly a goddess, with one arm upraised in a threatening attitude. Within what is left of her shell, heavily encrusted with bird-droppings and worm-mold, our diggers uncovered a fragment of script, in blocked letters or signs, which Bes Nef has translated: "Keep off the . . ." [2]

As far as can be ascertained, the name of this goddess—or giantess—was "Lib," or "Libby." [3] It is interesting and possibly rewarding to compare this figure to that of the "proprietor" or goddess of the temple-estate of Comana in Upper Cappadocia in the centuries preceding the death of Mithridates Eupator. This goddess, for whom no exact equivalent has been found in either the Greek or Latin pantheons, or, for that matter, among the deities of Erech, Akad, Sidon, or Palmyra, was

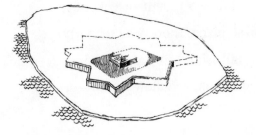

[2]*There was also found an inscription which Sra. Bess Nebby renders as follows: "I lift the lamp [damp?] beside [beyond?] the golden door." Could the sign "lift" or "left" actually be an anagram for "felt"; thus: "I felt the damp beyond the golden door"? (Ed.)*

[3]*See Kowly,* BERTY AMONG THE BRYTHONS *(Nairobi, 7857).*

PLATE III.

an ample female figure, armed to the teeth, and known simply as "Ma." The relationship of "Ma" to "Lib," or "Libby," is obscure; but it cannot be ruled out altogether.[4]

The second inscription, found in the east levels of the n.Yok excavation, reads (again according to Bes Nef): "The dodgers were shut out."[5]

So one must believe, on the face of it, that the Weans were an inhospitable people, who preferred to be left alone, and to shut out, as far as possible, the world around them.

We now come to certain findings in two small mounds to the north and east of the Valley of the Sun, both excavated by a team led by Hanh Shui and working under a grant from the Konegi Foundation at Kenya.

[4]*See Nef-Wiley, "Ma-ism among the Weans,"* RUWENZORI QUAR-TERLY, *XXII* (7859), *1–37.*

[5]*There is a legend that a small tribe known as dodgers (see Afrikaans "Broeklins" ([obs.] Ed.), having been obliged to leave the east coast, attempted to set up a home base or "penant" in the west, with what success is not known.*

In one mound, at the third level, a large, shallow bowl or concave wheel was dug up, into which had been cut a series of slots or grooves, each with a number from one to thirty-six, and with the addition of a zero and double zero. Eretebbe is of the opinion that this wheel, or disk, was used, like the Tibetan abacus, to subtract and divide. A primitive form of mathematics, indeed; but we have no reason to believe that the Weans excelled in any of the sciences.

It was in the same mound that our excavators uncovered the famous inscription: "Pomder Roo . . ."

We have been unable to find any translation of the glyph "Pomder," or any other inscription using the sign "Roo." However, by going back to the Hittite, Bes Nef (remembering how the "m" and "n" are often interchangeable, and how, among the Weans with their small collection of glyphs and hieroglyphs, one sign is often repeated in close succession, such as in the word "mommser") believes the sign actually denotes a room in which to ponder, or, in other words, a school.

As a matter of fact, a further find in the same general area bears out Bes Nef's contention that this was indeed a meeting place for young females. This find consists of several glyphs scratched upon a piece of glass which may at one time have been used for a mirror. The scratching is with a red material with a base of grease, which has apparently kept the glyph intact in the dry air. The exact meaning is obscure; it appears to be, among other things, the sign for a small fruit known as "the date."

Pound-Laundry is in itself the richest of the diggings. It is believed that at one time this city (for recent excavations indicate "the laundry," as we call it, to have been a city of considerable size) may even have been the capital of We itself, or at least to have had some political and historic importance. Obelgerst-Levy translates the first word of the name as "washing"; the second is obviously the sign for "weight." [6] It is not known what—if anything—was washed there.[7]

[6]*A ton? Bes Nef believes this weight to have been considerable.*

[7]*It should be noted here that an expedition under Hulay-Beneker has been for several seasons in the field, in search of a mound covering a lost city believed to have been more influential in Wean affairs than Pound-Laundry itself. Its name—as deci-*

The remains of temples of considerable size in the second and third layers at both Pound-Laundry and n.Yok give proof, if that were needed, that the Weans were essentially a religious people. However, it is now believed, in the light of later findings, that each city-state worshipped a different Divinity, and that the Pops of Bosstin (or Boxton) was not, as earlier believed, the Hops of M'lwawki. In the Valley of the Sun we have uncovered evidence that the inhabitants worshipped a powerful Divinity named Hedda, or Lolly (the sign is obscure); the glyph for Hedda (Header?), or Hatta, suggests a two-headed (or two-hatted) deity, possibly female in nature.

Nonetheless, the Wean Divinity, in whatever form, remained a Wean, and spoke the Wean language.

Surrounded by infinite space, by endless galaxies, by stars and planets without number, these proud, simple-minded, and obstinate people continued to believe themselves the center of the universe and the particular concern of the Almighty.[8]

---

phered by both Eretebbe and Bes Nef—was Mil Town; so far no trace of it has been found.

[8]*"God is a Zulu."—Eretebbe.*

PLATE IV. *Sra. Bess Nebby and Obelgerst-Levy in the Valley of the Sun.*

Here, in transcription, is Bes Nef's account of a religious occasion, translated from scrolls found in the Valley:

"[for that] he did cause them . . . [by] rock and roll . . . to [give out] cries and screams . . . loudly . . . and . . . in the corridors [9]. . . in syncope [1]. . ."

The word "roll" or "rolls" suggests a feast, possibly a feast of communion on a grand scale. So far no one has been able to explain the presence of the word "rock."

However, it is apparent that the people came together, and were seized by an ecstasy of some sort in which they lost reason and decorum. This belief is further strengthened by another scroll found in the same tumulus, in which the scribe reports: "And the spirit came down."

So the evidence points to the fact that the Weans were a religious people. There is additional witness in a silver coin dug up in one of the smaller mounds, which carries the in-

---

[9]*"Columns"—Bollek. "Aisles"—Obelgerst-Levy.*

[1]*"Syncopation"—Obelgerst-Levy. But this makes no apparent sense.*

scription "In God We Trust"—or "Trusted." The translation is by the Bantu scholar Eretebbe; the tense of the verb "to trust" is obscure, since only the letters "trus" have survived.

Neither Eretebbe nor any other member of the Academy has as yet been able to discover what god was meant. It is extremely unlikely that these ancient people had only one; inscriptions found among the ruins of Pound-Laundry suggest, in fact, a number of religious differences among them.

There are definite traces of Hebrew culture in the ruins of n.Yok; and although nothing has so far been found to suggest Babylonian or early Egyptian influences, there are hints here and there of the Cyprian cult of Antinous, particularly among the arts.

It is probable, too, that the Weans worshipped, among others, a sort of horse-god or centaur. Professor Rass points out that the fragment unearthed at s.Nita, and known as the Rass fragment, contains the unmistakable glyph for "horse," and the simple statement: "Swaps [schnapps?] was first." Yet another glyph, found not far from s.Nita, is that of a bearded god; it, too, states that "Schwepps [schwaps?] was first." [2]

In this regard, it is interesting to note that in a fragment unearthed at Oleens, and known as the Oleens fragment, the

[2]*It is suggested by Obelgerst-Levy that these two statements, taken together, point to a hierarchy among the Wean gods, and that Schwaps, or Swaps—or Schweppes—who at first was last, later took first place, and—following t'Out's Law—subsequently lost it.*

word "schnapps" is written: "cocacola," which was the name of an Aztec root-deity.

In politics, we are on surer ground. It is possible to say with absolute certainty, from scrolls unearthed at Pound-Laundry, and also from the ancient city of Boxton, or Bosstin, known to archaeologists as mound x-5, that the Weans were divided into hegemonies or states, loosely joined in a confederacy under one ruler (who, however, was not a theocrat) whose duty it was to retire after an interval varying in length from four to twelve years, and to issue warnings or oracles. These groups, or states, were divided into counties which were in turn divided into wards and precincts either for reasons of taxation, or for police. These divisions and subdivisions, whose chiefs were known both by the Roman name of Senator, and the Moorish name of Sherif, were also ruled by Queens.

There seem to have been many such Queens among the Weans. So far we have uncovered evidence of over seventy, such as—to name only a few—the Memphis Queen, the Queen of the Klondike, the Pepperdine Queen, and the Queen of Homecoming. As a matter of fact, there have been more Queens uncovered than we have communities to account for them. Where, for instance, was the community or ethnic group known as the Union of Press Lithographers Local 27? Or the Puddlers and Steamfitters Central? Or the Dress Designers International? They had their Queens.

That royal rule in We was precarious at best is attested to in the despairing cry of Mrs. Helen Sonnenberger, found in the fourth level of the Valley of the Sun: "I was Queen for a day." One ponders the fate of this woman, who reigned for so short a time. In this regard, Sra. Bess Nebby's translation of a "ho-fa" inscription, in linear B script, from the third level of the Cha'ago diggings, is of considerable interest and even importance. "This hofa," [3] says the unknown writer, "having triumphed over those who [did] oppose him, did [bring] together in union all that moved."

Neither Sra. Bess Nebby nor Sri. B'Han Bollek has ever found another mention of a hofa, although a number of

---

[3] *"hofa," from the Afrikaans; a kind of boss, or baas; obs. (Ed.)*

signs for boss or baas have been uncovered both in the Pound-Laundry diggings, at M'dtroit, and at h'Boken. It is possible that a hofa was a captain or a leader of a group, elected to wage war, and that having won an important battle he brought his people into a great union. That he was a strong leader in his day is attested to by the fact that "they could not get nine to go against him." (M'dtroit collection.)

Nevertheless, the probabilities are that he did not rule over We, since his capital was in or near Cha'ago,[4] and not at Pound-Laundry. The high rulers of We are for the most part unknown, a possible exception being a baas named Ike, whose peaceful remark, preserved for posterity, was "I like Ike."

[4]*We cannot be sure what the Weans of Cha'ago looked like. Although several paintings, badly discolored, have been unearthed near the Lakes, proving that the inhabitants were not entirely without visual art, one finds no recognizable human face or figure. They portray only squares, lines, lozenges, and mathematical figures; perhaps they were used in some way by the astrologers of the period.*

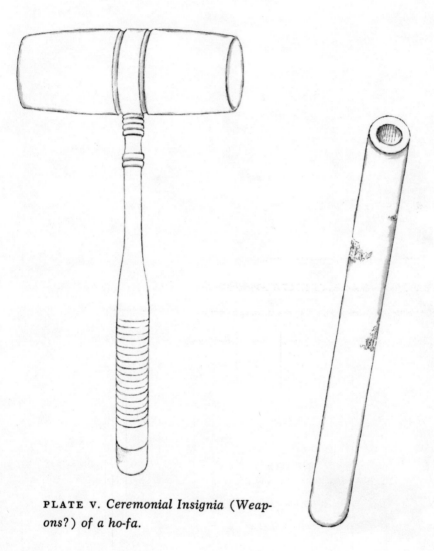

PLATE V. *Ceremonial Insignia (Weapons?) of a ho-fa.*

In the autumn of 7856, a workman digging among the shards and artifacts of the third level at n.Yok uncovered parts of a scroll which, perhaps, sheds some light upon the household arrangements of these primitive people. Much of the scroll is indecipherable, but one fragment, in linear script, seems to be part of a message, or letter, and states that "the Gomans have a little man who is very reasonable." A week later a similar fragment was unearthed south of Pound-Laundry at Pound-Charles; it declares: "We have a little man [to whom] we go for tickets."

Who were these little men? We know that slavery flourished in prehistoric times, both among the Babylonians and the Brythons. The historian F'eis believes that they may have been pygmies from our own ancient equatorial forests; but the O'Kona Wibalee prefers to link them to the "little people" of the north-Brythonic or Gaelic legends.

The Weans appear to have set a "high" table, though

Reconstructed lavatorium from artifacts found at Oleens, now on view in the Museum at Kenya.

not perhaps as high as those of other peoples, notably the Romans and the Gauls. Like the Parthians, they ate dogs, roasted, with horseradish or mustard; they cultivated greens of various kinds; they understood the art of viniculture. From their grapes they trod out a wine of sufficient strength, and from their corn they distilled a meadlike liquor which they mixed with a forest sap called "branch water." Unlike the Romans, they bathed in private, in small troughs and porcelain tureens.[5] They did not use the bidet, but did, as we have seen, make use of other formidable installations.

Due to the winter storms, work among the excavations in the north and northeast of the Great West Continent was suspended during the winters of 7856 and '57, and the teams led by Hulay Beneker and Hanh Shui turned their archaeological explorations to the south and west, notably in the Oleens tumulus, and the mounds of the Valley of the Sun. In the Valley, Hanh Shui brought up a "tab," or what appears to be a primitive form of banking; the meaning of the horizontal

[5]*See Bes Nef's monograph,* THE COMPANY OF CRANES, *and Kowly's analysis* (loc. cit.) *of the Kohler fragment. (Ed.)*

glyphs is not clear, but the vertical signs beneath them appear to spell out the names of men (or women) and, as such, are of interest to the historian.

	G	AB	R	H	HR	RBI	Pct
Snider	59	193	21	59	6	25	306
Gilliam	72	280	39	73	1	26	261
Reese	30	89	14	22	1	12	247
Jackson	26	47	7	10	1	4	213
Di Maggio	34	70	10	21	3	11	300

During the winter of '57, excavations in the south and southwest uncovered several large bowls, or stadia, and one battered metal cylinder on which is etched the mysterious sign: BUDWEISER.

The relationship of the sexes, known in We as "marriage," was advantageous to the female, and usually of short duration. An inscription found by Sri. B'Han Bollek in the diggings north of the Valley, and translated by Professor Kowly, reads as follows: "I was dissatisfied . . . and received in settlement . . . five million."

This is followed by a slightly larger fragment: " . . . having [presented] evidence [of] cruelty, the judge awarded to me [in settlement] by the month, two thousand . . . and I did [get] to keep the mink [and] also the jaguar." [6]

Needless to say, these fragments are from the writing-points of Wean women. There is no evidence of the male Wean ever receiving anything in settlement.

Nevertheless, he appears again and again in the same situation, apparently in no wise disheartened by what has happened to him. [7]

[6] *This zoological reference ("the jaguar") is of interest to those who profess to see a connection between the Wean and the slightly earlier Mayan or Aztec culture. (Ed.)*

[7] *Obelgerst-Levy believes that the Wean male feared the Wean female, since what he had, he could lose, and she could not. In this regard, the serious student is referred to Chaka's* BOOK OF THE ZULU: *"The honest man is always at a disadvantage." (Ed.)*

Premarital status among the Weans also had its establishments, if a touching little note scribbled on a piece of slate is to be believed. The entire inscription, lively and innocent, reads as follows: "I am gong stedy wit my frend Fredy. ruth, Agd 6."

In the Valley of the Sun we often find the sexual partner referred to as "a friend." This is not true in other communities; in Pound-Laundry in particular, the term "friend" is unknown.

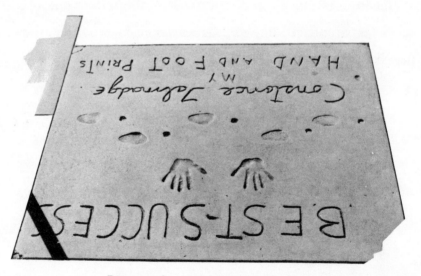

Pictographs unearthed in the forecourt of a temple in the Valley of the Sun. An obvious defacement of the ediface by children at play.

For an elderly Wean to take pleasure in the company of a nubile female of twelve or thirteen was considered a crime. In this, if in nothing else, the Weans were unlike all other people.

One of the paradoxes of Wean civilization is that the Wean considered himself uniquely capable of love. He also proclaimed himself the champion of liberty. In this regard the studies made by Obelgerst-Levy raise an interesting point: what liberties did the Wean himself enjoy? "He was unique," says Obelgerst-Levy, "in that he believed whatever he was told. But whatever liberties he championed for others, they did not include the right of hospitality.[8] What liberties he himself enjoyed are equally unknown; there is, from time to time, among the scrolls unearthed at Pound-Laundry some mention of a 'bill of rights' (or 'rites'), but the meaning of the phrase is unclear. Whether, as Hanh Shui believes, this bill was actually part of the public debt, it appears to have had no relation to the individual."

Nevertheless, the Wean artisan or worker lived what must

[8]*See comment on the goddess "Lib," p. 16. (Ed.)*

The Diggings at M'lwawki.

seem to us a comfortable and well-cared-for life. But that the majority of Weans were wealthy is not at all likely. Wean fortunes were for the most part self-made, and few indeed escaped the omnipresent tax-gatherer. On the other hand, a curious note in the Wean economy is struck by an inscription from the diggings at M'lwawki. "For that," it states, "I *did not grow my wheat,* [I did] receive seventy-five thousand . . ."

One is tempted to believe that the Weans did find a way to escape poverty after all, though so far no one has been able to understand it. In any case, one is forced to conclude from inscriptions found at Nassaw, that the most admired citizens were not men of wealth, but lived in relative simplicity, and in a state of advanced study. Unfortunately, none of their studies have come down to us.

It is true that two scrolls, bound each in oblong form, were found by the team of Haph-Bukong and Sumer, digging one winter among the ruins of what may once have been some sort of library. That it may have been a repository of many such scrolls—or, as we should say, books—is suggested by the remains of metal shelves which may have held the scrolls (or, alternatively, jellies, though informed opinion veers toward the scrolls).

Unfortunately, both scrolls, though easily legible, due to the brilliant work of the scholars Bes Nef and Obelgerst-Levy, are unintelligible; that is to say, the words, although translatable, make no sense when put together. One of these scrolls appears to be an account of a god or hero named Finigan, or

Finnegan; the size of the scroll and its rare state of preservation attest to its importance as a religious or historical document, but it is impossible to make out what happens to him. The second scroll is in what appears to be a metrical, or verse, form known as a dylan: nothing can be gathered from it at all.

A tablet unearthed at n.Yok gives us a welcome glimpse into business transactions in We. "[Having] borrowed a million," it reads in the transcription of B'Han Bollek, "[I acquired] thereby credit to twice that amount." This suggests an economy not unlike our own; one thinks of the motto of our Treasury Department: "To the Borrower, All." Throughout history there has never been anything more useful than credit, to establish credit. Without a debt, there is nothing.

The currency of the Weans consisted of the grand, the fin, the buck, the bit, and the payola.[9]

Like all ancient peoples, the Weans had their heroes, both legendary and actual, though it is sometimes hard to make

[9]*Obelgerst-Levy believes the payola to have been a small token of exchange, or favor, used mainly to acquire credit. See above.* (*Ed.*)

out, from the few scrolls and fragments in our possession, where legend ends and fact begins. There was an Alden, or Walden, who married the ruling deity of a pond, the nymph Sarsapriscilla, who endowed him with the power of tongues. "Speak for yourself, John," she is supposed to have said. This John, or Walden, is probably purely legendary and not to be confused with the John whose head, according to the Rolfe Inscription found in the Valley of the Rappahanock, was severed from his body by the giant Poco, or Little, Hondas.

Another John seems to have been a household deity connected with domestic, or family, comforts.[1]

The Weans were given to declarations of all kinds. In honor of one such "declaration" a yearly celebration was held during which bombs were exploded,[2] and vast quantities of dogs were roasted and consumed. What the declaration was, is not known; but the celebration, at its peak in the later years of the nineteenth century, seems to have died down by the middle of the twentieth.

[1]*See Kowly's analysis* (loc. cit.) *of the Kohler fragment.* (Ed.)

[2]*See the mariland fragment, Kenya Museum, B 215: ". . . and bombs bursting in air," k'Ubi transl.* (Ed.)

The actual material of these "declarations" is doubtful. In the Nassaw fragment there is a mention of a "poll," or "galop," which may have been a head-taking of some sort, possibly Tartar, or Maori, in origin. Such taking of heads may well have ended in a "declaration"—of what, we do not know.

The Museum at Kenya.

It is possible that the Weans themselves were not a warlike people, but that they were devoted nevertheless to violence, and self-pity. If this seems contradictory, one must remember that the most warlike of ancient people, the forest dwellers of the Oder and the Weser, also composed little songs about sadness, mother, and the Christmas tree.[3]

It is believed that the Weans attempted at one time to explore the regions of outer space, preferring this to explorations nearer at hand. However, it is not at all certain that they succeeded in getting off the ground, as there is no evidence of any higher studies in mathematics and physics which might have made such exploration possible. What they used to propel themselves upward and outward is uncertain; Obelgerst-Levy declares it to have been a zip gun.

If they did not excel in the sciences, they were nevertheless filled with imagination; it was enough for them to imagine something happening for them to believe that it had already happened. They did not so much await the fact as celebrate the intention. In this they were not unlike the Cycladaeans,

[3]"O TANNENBAUM," *the Kenya Catalogue, XXXII, 17, 3. (Ed.)*

who believed that they were immortal and chosen by the God —a belief to which they obstinately clung even while they were being exterminated by the Scythians. It is said that the Habiru shared this belief.

There is an inscription at present in the l'Ife Collection in the Museum at Uganda, taken from the fourth stratum at n.Yok, in which praise is given to the first Weans to travel in space, along with a description of their wives and families. From the style of this inscription, however, it is clear that the travelers had not yet left the surface of the earth.

Nevertheless, the Wean was no noodle; in fact, he was often critical of his government, and not afraid to say so. In the Minor Diary, a scroll found in the third level of the excavation at A'zusa, the writer, one Obit Minor, exclaims (in linear script B 2): "The nine old men have put their foot in it again." [4]

[4] *See Frazier-Bess Nebby,* GOLDEN BOUGH, *revised edition (Nairobi: Watusi Press; 7858), chapter on "Ceremonial Dances among the Ancients."*

It is possible that the "nine old men" made up a Council or Court of Elders, such as were to be found in the early history of the Zulu and the Kikuyu. But there is no evidence that the Weans accorded any extra privilege to age. When fully grown the Wean, both male and female, was expected to retire to some flowery beach, to a life of luxury and ease.[5]

Who Obit Minor was, we do not know; but we have reason to suspect that he was a writer who had been convinced of his own unimportance by three unimpeachable authorities: his publishers, the critics, and the public.

His life, as confided to the Diary, was arduous, being highly taxed, and without prizes. He sacrificed to the household gods, to Hedda (or Header) and Lolly, and to the high gods Hm'nway and Forkner (or Porkner). Domestic service being considered degrading among the freedom-loving Weans, he also did housework, a possible cause of biological confusion

---

[5]*See "How we retired on two hundred and fifty dollars a month for life," B'Han Bollek transl. (Johannisberg,* UNIVERSITY STUDIES, *XXVII,* 2397 seqq.)

which may have culminated in that ultimate disaster the facts of which we still hope to discover. These hopes have lately been stimulated by the translation, by Sra. Bess Nebby, of a portion of the Diary in which Obit mentions a "lost" generation. Is it possible that an entire age-group started off for parts unknown, and was never found again? His statement that this particular generation was for the birds [6] excites the imagination but does not, unfortunately, clarify matters.

So far we have been able to do little more than scratch the surface of life in WE or US. There is no answer to the riddle: who were the Weans? and no solution to the mystery of their disappearance. They left no pyramids, like the Egyptians; no laws, like the Romans; no temples, like the Greeks; no God, like the Jews. Their gravestones are simply the mounds on the Great West Continent.

Nor is it known how or why the Weans passed out of life and out of prehistory. They may have been destroyed by another group of tribes, known (in the Pound-Laundry collec-

[6]*"beards"? See reference to bearded figures with trumpets, p. 9. (Ed.)*

PLATE VI.

tion) as the More We (More Us or Usser). There is, in fact, one fragment in the collection which reads: "Between US and the USSR there can be no . . ." (Bes Nef's translation).

That they perished in a disaster of some kind many thousands of years ago is clear from an inscription among the ruins uncovered at n.Yok, which Sri. B'Han Bollek translates as follows: "Nor [north?] rain nor heat nor gloom of night . . ."[7] There are some hieroglyphics missing, and the inscription ends with the phrase " . . . their appointed rounds."

It must be remembered that the "r" and the "w" are readily interchangeable, both in Hittite and in ancient Hivite, and Bes Nef prefers the reading: "their pointed wounds." This naturally suggests a catastrophe, possibly an invasion from the East, perhaps by those very "More Weans," or "Ussers." On the other hand, if, as some (including B'Han Bollek) believe, the phrase should be read "their appointed rounds," the meaning of the full inscription might well be as follows: "The

---

[7]*The use of the sign for "rain," followed by the sign for "heat," suggests a meteorological disaster, such as a killing fog, or smog. (Ed.)*

north rain,[8] the heat and the gloom [doom?] of night [fright?] have accomplished their appointed rounds [or tasks]"—in other words, have annihilated the inhabitants.[9]

To return, however, to the "pointed wounds" of Bes Nef. In several of the larger mounds there have been unearthed many bronze, tin, and even stone figures of what would seem to be a kind of huge praying mantis. There are many groups of such figures, usually including male and female, and some-times with young; it is curious that in every case the male figure is larger and more powerful than the female, which we know to be untrue in the case of the actual praying mantis. These figures nevertheless have the small, cruel head, the long, savage arms, the spindly legs, and the attenuated bodies

[8]*"damp"? See* supra, *p. 15. (Ed.)*

[9]*Another theory, brought forward by Obelgerst-Levy, is to this effect: the "they" of this inscription stands for watchers or guardians of a post, i.e., postmen; that the bad weather, and other reasons, caused them to attend to their posts in a more and more desultory manner, ending up in what was probably a complete collapse of the entire post department.*

PLATE VII. *A mauran (mantis?): metal figure in the n.Yok collection.*

of the mantis. Is it possible that a civilization of men and women more or less like ourselves [1] might have been overwhelmed by an invasion of mantislike insects? Where could they have come from? and where did they go? The conjecture is, of course, fascinating; but no mantis skeletons or remains have been found, except the above-mentioned statues.

It is also true that several stone and marble objects, shaped like pretzels, with holes in them, have been uncovered among the eastern mounds. That these are not, as first thought, outhouses or natural stone formations, but man-made artifacts, is the theory of Hanh Shui, from a study of their surfaces, which appear to bear the marks of a chisel or some other sharp instrument. Some of these forms also display a sign, or glyph, for what Hanh Shui translates as a down, or moor; but which Obelgerst-Levy for some reason defines as a hennery.

Whether the Weans fought their wars in good spirit, or against their will, they must have been reasonably successful

[1] *"Less"—Obelgerst-Levy.*

—until the last war, which may have been waged, as noted, against the praying mantis. Yet there is no trace of a mantis civilization imposed upon the ruins of We.

What happened to the victors? And if not the mantis, who were the last great enemies of these ancient people?

Did the Weans, perhaps, try to buy them off at the end— and fail? It is entirely possible. Such a hypothesis is, in fact, strongly suggested by the trujillo fragment,[2] from which we learn that the young prince of a small foreign power spent upon a certain frito named Mercedes Benz a sum equal to that which his father, the Tyrant, received in tribute from We.

But as to the history of these almost unknown ancestors of ours,[3] no more is known than is known of the Romans and, later, the Brythons: they established themselves in the land by killing off the native tribes already there, and built their empire by the sword; when the sword rusted, they perished,

[2]*"trujillo": a frito; a small, fried sweet. (Ed.)*

[3]*Nat Obelgerst-Levy denies that the Weans were ancestors of ours.*

along with Egypt, Babylon, and Greece, leaving behind them only these curious mounds, some scrolls, Lib (or Libby), a few monuments and glyphs, some statues of eggs and mantises, and no music.

My grateful thanks to my friend Dan Laurence,

who edited this book for me

and saw it through the press.

ACKNOWLEDGMENT: Sra. Bess Nebby's clothes by Ruth Matthews; pre-Columbian gold thunderbird by courtesy of Ruth Matthews. "Mauran" (mantis?) on page 53 by Jean Paul Mauran, photographed by Wally White. Photographs on pages 23, 38, and 40 by Wally White. Photograph on page 34 by courtesy of The Bettman Archive. Photograph on page 44 by courtesy of FPG: Ruth Sondak.

A NOTE ABOUT THE AUTHOR

ROBERT NATHAN was born in New York City in 1894, and was educated at private schools in the United States and in Switzerland. While attending Harvard University, he was an editor of the *Harvard Monthly*, in which his first stories and poems appeared.

Except for two short periods during which he was a solicitor for a New York advertising firm and a teacher in the School of Journalism of New York University, Mr. Nathan has devoted his time exclusively to writing. He is the author of some thirty-six volumes of poetry and prose, and from this body of distinguished work he has acquired a reputation as a master of satiric fantasy unique in American letters. He lives now in California with his wife, Shirley.

A NOTE ON THE TYPE

The Text of this book was set on the Linotype in a new face called PRIMER, *designed by Rudolph Ruzicka, earlier responsible for the design of Fairfield and Fairfield Medium, Linotype faces whose virtues have for some time now been accorded wide recognition.*

The complete range of sizes of Primer was first made available in 1954, although the pilot size was ready as early as 1951. The design of the face makes general reference to Linotype Century (long a serviceable type, totally lacking in manner or frills of any kind) but brilliantly corrects the characterless quality of that face.

Composed by Kingsport Press, Inc., Kingsport, Tenn. Printed by Philip Klein, New York, bound by H. Wolff, New York. Paper manufactured by Mead Papers, Inc., New York. Typography, drawings, binding and jacket designs by George Salter.